Jack and the Beanstalk

CW00840322

CHARACTERS

Mother

Narrator

Old woman

Giant's wife

Jack

Giant

Hen

(The Old woman, Hen and the Harp could be played by the same person.)

Harp

SCENE 1

(The little cottage where Jack and his mother live.)

| Narrator | Once upon a time there lived a poor woman who had a son called Jack. They did not have much money. All they had was a cow called Daisy. But there came a time when they ran out of food.

Jack There's no food left. What will we do, Mother?

Mother We will have to sell Daisy. Take her to market and get as much money as you can for her.

Narrator So the next day, Jack went off with Daisy. He had not gone far when he met an old woman.

Old woman Good morning, Jack. Where are you off to?

Jack I'm going to market to sell this cow.

Old woman I'll buy your cow.

Jack How much will you give me? Will you give me five gold coins?

Old woman *(holding out her hand)* I'll give you something better than five gold coins. These beans are magic. You can have them if you wish and I will have your cow.

Jack Five magic beans will be much better than five gold coins! Here, take the cow and give me the beans.

Old woman Here you are. Carry them carefully back home.

Mother That didn't take you long, Jack. I see the cow has gone. How much did you get for her?

Jack *(counting out the beans into Mother's hand)* One, two, three, four, five. I got these! They are magic beans.

Mother You silly boy! Those beans are not magic. Now we have nothing!

Narrator And she took the beans and threw them out of the window.

SCENE 2

Jack   Oh, how stupid I've been!

Narrator   Jack got no supper that night. He went to bed hungry. The next day, when he woke up, everything looked dark. He jumped up and went over to the window.

Jack   What's this? What's going on out there?

Narrator   Growing up into the sky were five beanstalks climbing round and round one another. However hard he looked, Jack couldn't see the top.

Jack   Mother, I am going to climb up the beanstalk.

Mother   Oh, be careful, Jack!

Narrator   So Jack began to climb the beanstalk, up and up through the clouds.

Jack   At last I'm at the top. And there's a path through the leaves!

Narrator Jack followed the path for a long time.
Then he came to a very big house.

Jack I'll bang on the door.
BANG! BANG! BANG!

10

Narrator A tall woman opened the door.

Giant's wife What do you want?

Jack Please could I have some dinner? I'm hungry.

Giant's wife Oh no! My husband is a giant, and he eats people like you. He will be home soon.

Jack Well, I'm not going away until I get some dinner.

Giant's wife Oh, very well, then. You can come in and have some bread and cheese. But be quick!

Narrator   Jack had just stopped eating when he heard a THUMP! THUMP! THUMP! The house shook.

Giant's wife   *(opening the oven door)* Quick! That's my husband. Get in here.

Narrator   Jack got into the oven, just as the giant came in.

Giant Fee fi fo fum.
I smell the blood of an Englishman.

Giant's wife Oh no you don't! Go and sit at the table.

Narrator So the giant sat down and ate his dinner.

Giant Now I'm going to count my gold.

Narrator The giant counted the gold coins, then he put his head on the table and went to sleep.

Jack *(climbing out of the oven)* I'll have that sack of gold!

Narrator So Jack picked up the sack of gold as quietly as he could, ran back down the long path and climbed all the way back down the beanstalk.

Jack Mother! Mother!
Look what I've got!

Mother Oh, Jack! Look at all this gold!
You are a clever boy!

SCENE 3

Narrator Soon Jack wanted to climb the beanstalk again. So up he went, through the clouds and along the long path to the big house.

Giant's wife What do you want? Didn't I let you in before? And didn't you run off with our gold?

Jack No, not me! Please let me in. I would like a drink of milk and some pie.

Giant's wife Oh, very well. Come in. But be quick – don't let my husband catch you.

Narrator Just then Jack heard a THUMP! THUMP! THUMP! The house shook.

Giant's wife *(opening the oven door)* Quick! That's my husband. Get in here.

Narrator Jack got into the oven, just as the giant came in.

Giant **Fee fi fo fum.**
I smell the blood of an Englishman.

Giant's wife Oh no you don't! Go and sit at the table.

Narrator So the giant sat down and ate his dinner.

Giant That was a good dinner, wife! Now give me my magic hen.

Giant's wife Here it is, husband.

Giant Come on, magic hen. Lay!

Hen CLUCK!

Narrator The hen laid a golden egg.

Hen CLUCK! CLUCK! CLUCK!

Narrator Again and again the hen laid its golden eggs until the giant put his head down on the table and went to sleep.

Jack *(climbing out of the oven)* I'll have that magic hen.

Narrator So Jack put the magic hen under his arm and the golden eggs in his pocket. As fast as he could, he ran all the way back to the beanstalk and climbed down it.

Jack Mother! Mother! Look what I've got!

Mother Well done, Jack!
We are rich now.
Very rich.

SCENE 4

Narrator Soon Jack wanted to climb the beanstalk again. So up he went, through the clouds and along the long path to the big house. But this time he didn't go to the door. He stayed outside until the giant's wife came out to get her washing off the line.

Jack I'll just run inside and hide in the oven.

Narrator The woman came in. She put the giant's dinner on the table. Then Jack heard a THUMP! THUMP! THUMP! The giant walked into the room.

Giant **Fee fi fo fum.**
I smell the blood of an Englishman.

Giant's wife Do you?

| **Giant** | Oh yes I do. Where can he be? SNIFF, SNIFF, SNIFF. I can't find him anywhere. |

| **Narrator** | So the giant sat down and ate his dinner. |

| **Giant** | That was a good dinner, wife! Now give me my golden harp. |

| **Giant's wife** | Here it is, husband. |

| **Giant** | Come on, golden harp. Sing to me! |

| **Harp** | La, la, la, la, la... |

| **Narrator** | The golden harp sang songs to make the giant laugh, and songs to make him cry. Then it sang a song that sent the giant to sleep. |

Jack *(climbing out of the oven)* I'll have that golden harp.

Harp Help! Help! Help!

Giant *(waking up)* What's that? What's going on?

Jack Oh no! He's seen me!

Giant Hey! Stop, that's my harp!

Harp Help! Help! Help!

Narrator	Jack ran back to the beanstalk. He jumped on to the beanstalk and the giant jumped on after him. The beanstalk shook.
Jack	*(shouting)* Mother! Get me the axe! I'm coming down.
Mother	Ooooh, be careful, Jack.
Narrator	At last Jack got to the bottom. He took hold of the axe and CHOP! CHOP! CHOP! He began to cut down the beanstalk.

Giant Oh no! I'm falling! Aaaargh!

Narrator Down came the beanstalk, and down came the giant, and that was the end of them. As for Jack and his mother, they were happy and rich for ever after.